Special features:

Phonically decodable text
builds reading confidence

Short sentences with
simple language

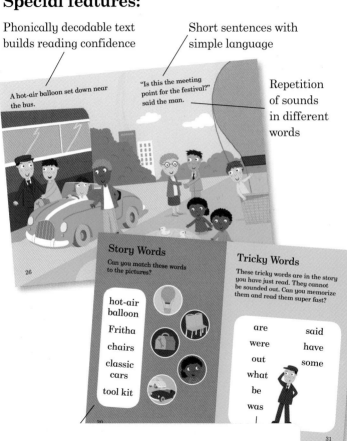

A hot-air balloon set down near
the bus.

"Is this the meeting
point for the festival?"
said the man.

Repetition
of sounds
in different
words

26

Story Words

Can you match these words
to the pictures?

hot-air
balloon

Fritha

chairs

classic
cars

tool kit

30

Tricky Words

These tricky words are in the story
you have just read. They cannot
be sounded out. Can you memorize
them and read them super fast?

are	said
were	have
out	some
what	
be	
was	
I	

31

Summ~~ary~~
reinfor~~ces~~

...that
...ed out

Educational consultant: Geraldine Taylor
Phonics and Book Banding Consultant: Kate Ruttle

LADYBIRD BOOKS

UK | USA | Canada | Ireland | Australia
India | New Zealand | South Africa

Ladybird Books is part of the Penguin Random House group of companies
whose addresses can be found at global.penguinrandomhouse.com.

www.penguin.co.uk   www.puffin.co.uk   www.ladybird.co.uk

Penguin
Random House
UK

First edition published 2020
001

Copyright © Ladybird Books Ltd, 2020

Printed in China

A CIP catalogue record for this book is available from the British Library

ISBN: 978-0-241-40513-0

All correspondence to
Ladybird Books
Penguin Random House Children's
80 Strand, London WC2R 0RL

Visiting Grandad

Written by Dr Christy Kirkpatrick
Illustrated by Hannah Wood

Mark and Fritha went to Grandad's for the weekend.

Grandad was a big sports fan.
Mark and Fritha saw Grandad
jumping high.

"Let's get some fresh air,"
said Grandad.

Grandad took Mark and Fritha
to the park. Grandad told them
how to get the ball in the goal.

Next, they went to the swimming pool. Grandad was a quick swimmer. The pool was a bit cool!

11

"There is a tower near the pool," said Grandad. "We can go there and run up the stairs."

It began to rain.

"Shall we go back to the flat?" said Mark.

"All right," said Grandad.

Grandad, Mark and Fritha
had fish and chips for dinner.
Then they all had a rest.

Mark and Fritha saw Grandad.
He had fallen asleep!

Story Words

Can you match these words
to the pictures?

Grandad

swimming
pool

chips

tower

football

Mark

Tricky Words

These tricky words are in the story you have just read. They cannot be sounded out. Can you memorize them and read them super fast?

he   said

we   they

was   all

The Car Festival

Written by Dr Christy Kirkpatrick
Illustrated by Hannah Wood

Grandad, Mark and Fritha were off to a car festival.

They sat on chairs at the top of the bus.

Bang! The bus let out a sudden hiss and groan.

Wait! What was that?

Are we at the bus stop?

Grandad let out a sigh.
"I think we are stuck," he said.

Some classic cars were
next to the bus.

A hot-air balloon set down near the bus.

Mark and Fritha had a turn in the balloon. They had a look at the classic cars.

By now, it was getting dark.

"The car festival will be shut now,"
said Grandad.

"We had a festival right
near the bus!" said Fritha.
"It was the best bus
trip ever!"

Story Words

Can you match these words
to the pictures?

hot-air
balloon

Fritha

chairs

classic
cars

tool kit